GROLIER

Your partner in education

Distributed by Grolier, Sherman Turnpike
Danbury, Connecticut 06816

Grolier offers a varied selection of
children's book racks and tote bags.
For details on ordering, please write:
Grolier Direct Marketing
Sherman Turnpike
Danbury, CT 06816
Att: Premium Department

My b Book

by Jane Belk Moncure

illustrated by Linda Hohag

THE CHILD'S WORLD

Mankato, MN 56001

Little  had a box.

"I will fill my  box."

Little put on a bonnet.

She went for a walk.

Little  found a bird and a birdbath.

She put them into her box.

Little ![b] found a bunny.

Did she put the bunny into her box?

She did.

Little **b** found a bee.

She put the bee into her box.

Then she found a . . .

baby baboon.

and a big banana.

"In you go," said Little b.

The box was full.

Then she found a

bicycle

with a 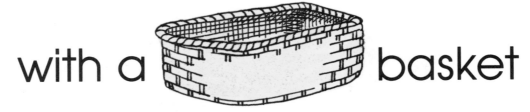 basket

on it.

She put her  into

the basket.

She rode away.

But the  baby baboon,

the bunny,

the bird,

and the box fell off

the bicycle.

Little  fell off too.

"That was a bad bump," she said.

Then she
found a  ball and
a bat.

"Let's play ball," she said.

The baby baboon
hit the ball.

A bear found it.

"Bear,"
said Little .

"Give me
the ball."

22

Then she put all her
things into her box.

She
put
the
bear
in
too.

"My box is too full.

It may break," said Little b.

24

She rode over
a bridge.

25

She found a big boat.

"The boat is just right for all my things," she said.

And it was!

More words with Little .

balloon

barn

butterfly

bathtub

bell

bug

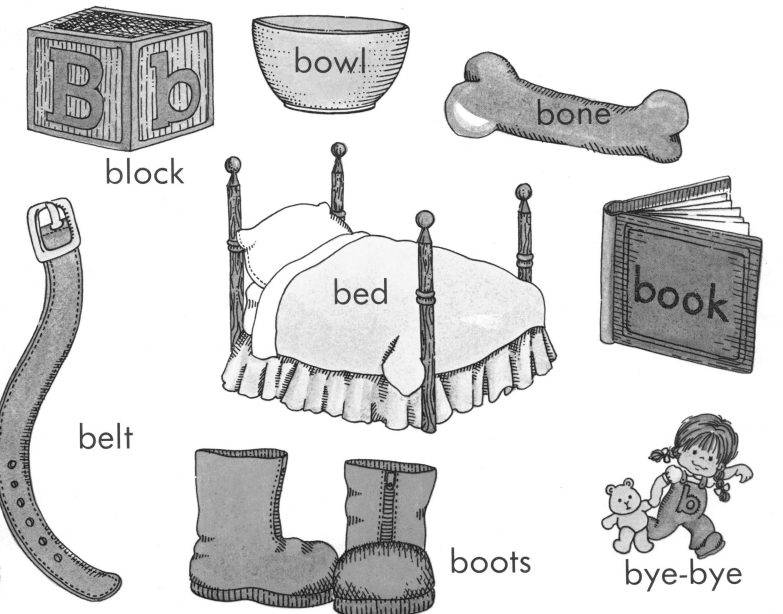

block

bowl

bone

belt

bed

book

boots

bye-bye

29